C000112698

Practise

Grammar

KS3

Age 11–14

Ron Simpson

Contents

Introduction

How does this book deal with grammar?

Grammar is the way in which the English language is put together. This book is divided into two halves. The first half, **parts of speech** (pages 3–14), examines five main parts of speech: nouns, pronouns, verbs, adjectives and adverbs. It deals with how these are formed and, most of all, with their *functions*, the jobs they do in a sentence. The second half, **forming sentences** (pages 19–30), tells you how to join the parts of speech together to form different types of sentences. These sections also deal with other parts of speech (conjunctions, prepositions) whose job it is to link together different parts of a sentence.

How to use *Practise*

If you need to *practise*, this book explains the most important points, then provides exercises to check your understanding. Before you start, you will need an exercise book of your own for copying and completing the exercises. As you work through the book, when you are confident that you have answered all the questions in an exercise correctly, move on to the next stage. If you feel you need more practice, follow a different explanation until you understand. On *Try it yourself!* pages you should do the activity *before* reading the notes at the side. When you are ready, photocopy the middle four pages of this book so that you can cut them up and do the activities. Make sure you keep the pieces in a safe place, such as an envelope, so that you do not lose them.

First published in 2007
exclusively for WHSmith by
Hodder Education, an Hachette UK company,
338 Euston Road
London NW1 3BH

Impression number   10 9 8 7 6 5 4 3
Year   2010
Text and illustrations © Hodder Murray 2007

Cover illustration by Sally Newton Illustrations

Typeset by Fakenham Photosetting Limited, Fakenham, Norfolk

Printed and bound in Italy

A CIP record for this book is available from the British Library

ISBN 978 0 340 94285 7

Nouns

Get started

The first half of this book deals with **parts of speech**.

The term 'part of speech' defines what job or function a word has within a sentence. Many words have different functions because they can be used as more than one part of speech. It is a good idea to know the correct terms. Look at these two sentences:

This description has some really vivid adjectives.
This description has some words to tell us about the things really vividly.

Which one reads (and sounds) better?

Practice

A **noun** is the name of a person, thing, place, feeling, mood, idea, etc.

To begin with, there are two main types of nouns:

Common	Proper
town	Burnley
friend	Rebecca
continent	Africa
supermarket	Tesco
castle	Windsor

Can you work out the difference between a common noun and a proper noun?

- A **common noun** is the name shared by a whole group of people, places or things.
- A **proper noun** is an individual name.
- Proper nouns begin with capital letters; common nouns do not.

The words *common* and *proper* both have several meanings:

- *Common*, in this case, means 'shared by all'. Think of *common land* or, as a noun, *the common*. A common noun is a name common to everything within that group.
- *Proper*, when referring to nouns, means 'own' in the sense of 'your own' or 'my own'. Of course, there are thousands of boys and men called *John*, but all Johns recognise it as 'their own' name.

Grammar and syntax

You may have come across the word *syntax*. This is quite a difficult word which you do not need to remember, but to avoid confusion, it is worth explaining what it means.

Syntax could be described as 'the grammar of a sentence'.

- *Grammar* explains the different parts of a language.
- *Syntax* explains how they are put together in a sentence.

The second half of this book deals with syntax, but as most people think of it as part of grammar, this is the last reference to syntax in this book.

Definite and indefinite article

Most common nouns make great use of the **definite article** (*the*) and the **indefinite article** (*a* or, before a vowel sound, *an*). If a common noun is in the singular (only one), an article is essential. For the plural (more than one), the indefinite article is not used:

The car is in the garage.
The cars are in the garage.

We decided to hire a car.
We've hired cars throughout Europe.

What does a noun do?

Think about what language is for.

To begin with, it tells us things or asks about things.

Very often it is a matter of identifying somebody or something and saying what he/she/it/they did.

So two of the main jobs for a noun (not the only ones) are as subject and object for a sentence:

The train left the station.

Train and *station* are both nouns. *Train* is the subject (the doer of the action) and *station* is the object (what the action was done to).

The sections Forming sentences: subject and verb and Direct and indirect objects go into this in more detail.

Try it yourself!

Find the nouns

See if you can find 15 nouns in the following sentences. When you have found a noun, write it in your exercise book under one of two headings: **Proper nouns** and **Common nouns**. (Note: the capital letters have been left off the proper nouns. Make sure that you use capitals when you write them out.)

> The last match was between brentford and barnet.
> We saw ahmed in the park.
> My favourite character in a book is harry potter.
> The best lesson of the day is english.
> My parents wanted to go to spain, but my brother preferred greece.

Check your answers on **pages 31–32**.

All correct?

If not, look back at the definitions of common and proper nouns.

Sometimes, a proper noun may have more than one word (*Harry Potter*). Some are even longer, and sometimes the less important words do not have a capital letter:

Prince of Wales   News of the World

Choose your nouns

Copy the following sentences into your exercise book and then add your own choice of nouns to them. In each case, try one version with a proper noun and one with a common noun (which might need a definite or indefinite article):

_____ Ahmed _____ reached the top of _____ Mount Versuvius _____.
Next year, _____ DunTDM _____ will be very popular with _____ gaming _____.
I chose _____ Ryan _____ as _____ captain _____.
I agreed to look after _____ Gryffindor _____, but not _____ Slytherin _____.

There are, of course, no right answers, but a typical sentence might read:

Hillary reached the top of Everest. (proper nouns)
The expedition reached the top of the mountain. (common nouns)

Collective nouns and pronouns

Get started

If a noun refers to a group made up of a number of individuals, it is referred to as a **collective noun**.

So there might be a *herd* of cattle or a *flock* of birds, a football *team* or an education *committee*.

In your writing, it is important to remember that, if there is only one group (even if it is made up of hundreds of individuals), you should treat it as singular.

Look at these three examples:

The players <u>were waiting</u> for the kick-off. (plural – more than one)
The team <u>was waiting</u> for the kick-off. (singular – only one team)
The teams <u>were waiting</u> for the kick-off. (plural – two teams)

But see the note **Don't be ridiculous!** on the right.

Practice

It would be correct, but clumsy and unpleasant, to write:

Mrs Jenkins moved to Hatfield when Hatfield was still a village. Mrs Jenkins always claimed that Hatfield was the nicest place Mrs Jenkins had ever lived in. In later years, Hatfield grew into a large town and Mrs Jenkins enjoyed the chances Mrs Jenkins had to visit the range of shops in the High Street. But Mrs Jenkins thought Hatfield was spoiled by the number of gangs which Mrs Jenkins found rather frightening.

Too many mentions of *Mrs Jenkins* and *Hatfield*!

You could use *the town* sometimes, but your main help comes from *she*, *her* and *it*:

Mrs Jenkins moved to Hatfield when it was still a village. She always claimed that it was the nicest place she had ever lived in.

Words that take the place of nouns are called **pronouns**.

Personal pronouns

Singular	I, me	you	he, she, him, her, it
Plural	we, us	you	they, them

Now read the note **Subjects and objects** on the right.

The pronouns above are all **personal pronouns**; now read the note **Other pronouns** on page 6.

now read the note **Other pronouns** on page 6.

Don't be ridiculous!

Where possible, you must treat a singular collective noun as singular:

The committee <u>has</u> decided to appoint Ms Newman.

The flock of sheep <u>was</u> wandering into the valley.

The crowd <u>is</u> getting angry.

But this rule has a ridiculous side. For instance, strictly speaking, some football clubs (e.g. those ending in *City* or *United*) are singular. Others (e.g. *Rovers* or *Wanderers*) are plural. It obviously sounds silly to write:

Manchester City <u>is</u> safe from relegation, but Bolton Wanderers <u>are</u> still in danger.

Always remember the rule, but use your common sense as well.

Subjects and objects

In English, a noun stays the same whether it is subject or object.

Only word order tells us the difference between The bandit shot the sheriff and The sheriff shot the bandit.

However, personal pronouns (except for *you* and *it*) do change.

Remember: *I*, *he*, *she*, *we* and *they* are used for the subject of the sentence – what it is about, the doer of the action.

Me, *him*, *her*, *us* and *them* are used for the various forms of object – some form of 'done-to'. (See pages 21–22 for more on Direct and indirect objects.)

Other pronouns

The most common form of pronoun is the personal pronoun, but do not forget:

The word *pronoun* means 'instead of noun'.

So any word that does the job of a noun is a pronoun.

Look at this sentence:

The picture fell off the wall.

The first noun in the sentence, the subject of the sentence, is *picture*.

What takes the place of *picture* in this version?

This fell off the wall.

This, of course. It is taking the place of a noun, so in this example, *this* is a pronoun.

One more example:

Rachel and Sunita were late for school.

If two nouns are replaced with *both* (Both were late for school.) then *both* must be a pronoun.

Try it yourself!

Fill in the chart

Copy the chart below into your exercise book and fill it in by completing all the empty spaces.

For instance, if *dog* appeared in the **Common** column, you could add whatever dog's name you wanted under **Proper** and then put *pack*, the word for a group of dogs, under **Collective**.

Common	Proper	Collective
	Sergeant Marshall	
pupil		
		band
book		
politician		
		team
	Bambi	
singer		
		staff
ship		

Check your answers against the suggestions on **pages 31–32**.

There will be many differences, particularly in the **Proper** column.

Are you happy that your answers are right?

A quick look at pronouns

Copy this short paragraph into your exercise book and put a ring around every pronoun.

'I found this in the shed,' said Jamie to his father. 'What is it?' asked Mr Winstanley who was visiting them. 'It's an old copy of *Gardening World*,' said Jamie's dad. 'They used to be a great help to me and I never threw any away.' 'So you've kept them all from 20 years ago?' said Mr Winstanley, smiling as though he found something funny. 'Yes. I know, sad, isn't it?'

Check your answers on **pages 31–32**. Any mistakes?

Not surprising – some of these are very difficult. Read the explanations on the answers page carefully.

Verbs: being and doing

Get started

The simplest use of language consists of two things:
- identifying *who* or *what* you are talking about
- stating what he/she/it/they is/are doing.

Nouns ('naming words') do the first.
Verbs ('doing words') do the second.

Look at these sentences:

Emma (proper noun) **plays** (verb) **football every night**.
The gardener (common noun) **dug** (verb) **up the vegetable patch**.

However, it is not really as simple as that.
- There are other parts of a sentence to think about.
- Not all verbs are **verbs of doing**.

Practice

Often you want to tell your reader or listener what your subject is doing.

But, in many other cases, you want to say what she is like, where he is, who they are with or what sort of animal it is.

These need **verbs of being**.

The most common verb of being is *to be* which has some very strange forms:

Present: I am   you are   he/she/it is   we are   you are   they are
Past: I was   you were   he/she/it was   we were   you were   they were

Other common verbs of being include *seem* and *become.*

Look at the same sentence with the verbs *be*, *become* and *seem* in the same place.

Tom <u>was</u> angry when the test results came out.
Tom <u>became</u> angry when the test results came out.
Tom <u>seemed</u> angry when the test results came out.

They are all obviously doing the same job – as verbs of being.

To do or not to do?

One of the confusing things about English is that many words can be different parts of speech at different times. They can be identified by the job they are doing: their function.

There is one verb that is widely used as both a verb of being and a verb of doing. Read the following sentences and try to work out how this is so:

Just as we mentioned her name, Sonya appeared round the corner.

Mr Jones appeared worried by the inspector's presence.

Do you see the difference?

In the first sentence, Sonya did something; you could have used a word like *walked. Appeared* is a verb of *doing*.

In the second sentence, *appeared* is used to tell us what Mr Jones was like; you could have used *seemed.* This time it is a verb of *being*.

The subject didn't do it

When a verb of doing is 'done to' someone or something, it is possible to turn the sentence round:

Kirsty beat Rachel in the 100 metres race.

Rachel was beaten by Kirsty in the 100 metres race.

Or even, if you are only interested in Rachel and do not know or care who won:

Rachel was beaten in the 100 metres race.

In this case, the verb is formed by more than one word (*was beaten*): a part of the verb *to be* is used with the main verb (*beaten*).

This form (*was beaten*) is called the passive. The normal form (*beat*) is called the active.

The passive is useful when the person or thing suffering the action is the main focus of interest.

Do not over-use the passive. Using too many passive verbs can be clumsy and boring to read.

Try it yourself!

First find the verb . . .

Copy the following sentences into your exercise book. Each sentence has one verb in it. When you have found it, put a ring around it:

> I caught some fish in the pond behind our house.
> My father drives to work each day.
> Karen seemed happy with her new school.
> Ronan Keating opened the new shopping centre.
> I became very tired during the trip to the airport.
> Sara slipped on the icy pavement.

Check your answers on **pages 31–32**.

All correct?

Now copy out these sentences and add your own verbs:

> We all _____ the school bus.
> Shafique always _____ her History lessons.
> Our local team _____ the County Cup Final.
> The new youth leader _____ very pleasant.
> I _____ our new neighbours.
> The weather in Malta _____ to be improving.

A quick check

Without looking back, decide whether the verbs in the following sentences are **verbs of being** or **doing**. Copy them into your exercise book and write the type of verb you think each one is alongside:

> Middleton Parva <u>is</u> not on the map.
> Eventually I <u>found</u> it in the A to Z.
> My brother <u>appeared</u> in time for tea.
> As usual, he <u>appeared</u> hungry.
> At ten past nine, he <u>left</u> in a great hurry.
> He <u>seemed</u> anxious about something.
> The teachers <u>blamed</u> me for the damage.
> I <u>was</u> not responsible for the disturbance.

Check your answers on **pages 31–32**.

All correct?

If not, now is the time to turn back to **page 7** and go through **Verbs: being and doing** again.

Verbs: tenses

Get started

What time is it?

The form of the verb shows when events are taking/took/will take place. This is known as the **tense** of a verb. The main tenses are **present**, **simple past**, **perfect** and **future**. There are many more complicated tenses, but these are the ones that are used the most.

Practice

Present tense

This is very simple. It is the same as the basic form of the verb, except in the 3rd person singular. This is the most frequently used part of the verb which follows any singular noun or *he*, *she* or *it.* For this, add *-s* (occasionally *-es*). So: *I send, Mrs Desai sends.*

Future tense

This is also straightforward, but needs another verb to help out (an **auxiliary verb**). Mostly *will* is added to the basic verb. Sometimes *shall* is used, especially after *I*, but *will* is the most usual. So: *I will send, Mrs Desai will send.*

Simple past tense

Things become more complicated because verbs form the past tense in two different ways. The only way around this is simply to learn which verbs are which. Some add *-ed* (occasionally *-d* or *-t*) to the basic form: *wished, helped, hoped, burnt.* Altered versions of this include *sent* and *paid.* Others change the vowel in the middle: *shoot/shot, fight/fought, give/gave, come/came.* Some add *-d* or *-t* as well: *tell/told, buy/bought.*

Perfect tense

Like the future tense, this uses an auxiliary verb: *to have.* It is used with a part of the verb called the **past participle**: *I have sent, Mrs Desai has sent.* The past participle can be difficult: it is often (but not always) the same as the past tense. Watch out in particular for past participles ending in *-n* or *-en*: *I fell/I have fallen, she gave/she has given, the wind blew/the wind has blown, the flowers grew/the flowers have grown.*

The forms of tenses *are* confusing. Very often it is easiest to learn from examples and the exercises on **page 10** will help.

Go, went, gone

A real problem with English is that the most common words are often the oddest in form. The verb *to be* is a good example. So is *to go.* For some reason, the simple past of *to go* is *went.* The past participle then returns to something like normal: *gone.*

Remember to write *we have gone*, not *we have went*.

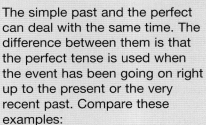

Two pasts

The simple past and the perfect can deal with the same time. The difference between them is that the perfect tense is used when the event has been going on right up to the present or the very recent past. Compare these examples:

Last year, I <u>started</u> a new school. (It happened a long time ago.)

I <u>have started</u> a new school. (You are giving someone the news.)

I <u>fell</u> down and hurt my knee. (There is no hint of when it happened.)

I <u>have fallen</u> down and hurt my knee. (You obviously want help *now*!)

On and on

There is a part of the verb called a present participle which ends in *-ing*. This has all kinds of uses and one of them is to form continuous tenses.

Continuous tenses suggest that, so far as the writer knows, the action is still going on. For example:

The car is running out of fuel.

It has not stopped yet, but there is no sign of a filling station either!

The idea of past continuous may not seem to make sense, but look at this example:

Mr Hopkins was cutting his grass when I passed last week.

He will not still be cutting it now! But, as you passed, the action was continuing. You have no idea how long he took. He may not even have finished; he may have left it when it started to rain. So the meaning is different from Mr Hopkins cut his grass last week.

Try it yourself!

Complete the chart

The chart below lists the present, simple past and perfect tenses of 20 verbs. In each case, we are looking for the 3rd person singular. The first one has been done for you – now write the headings and the rest of the verbs into your exercise book and fill in all the gaps.

	Present	Simple past	Perfect
find	he (or she) finds	he found	he has found
try			
lie (as in *lie down*)			
lie (not tell truth)			
lay (put down)			
force			
join			
beat			
enjoy			
be			
grow			
keep			
note			
write			
bite			
do			
show			
insist			
run			
draw			

Check your answers on **pages 31–32**.

All correct?

If so, congratulations – some of these were very difficult.

- Make sure you know the difference between *lie/lay* and *lay/laid*. This can be very confusing. You use *lay/laid* only when you are putting something down, setting a table, etc.

  I am going to lay the table. but **I am going to lie down.**
  The soldier laid down his arms. but **The soldier lay down exhausted.**

- Turn *y* into *i* if it follows a consonant, but not if it follows a vowel: *try/tried*, but *enjoy/enjoyed*.

Adjectives

Get started

Adjectives are often referred to as 'describing words'.

This is not completely true.

An adjective is a word that *adds something more* about a noun.

Practice

Sometimes a **noun** by itself is not enough. Imagine that you are in a crowded bus station and you are looking for the right bus. There is no point in asking about *the bus.* You need to use adjectives. Just imagine a few phrases from the conversation:

the <u>red</u> bus   <u>our</u> bus   <u>that</u> bus   the <u>next</u> bus   the <u>right</u> bus

- All the underlined words are adjectives.

- How many of them are describing words? Only *red*.

- What do they have in common? They help you to find the right bus by *adding something more* about the noun.

When reading, you can only find out what an adjective is (as a part of speech, not an individual adjective) by knowing what the noun is. So, when writing, it is usual to start with the noun – the name of a person, place, object, etc. – but that is not always enough detail.

- There may be more than one noun in the sentence.

- Writing can be boring if there are not enough details about characters, places, etc.

So look for and use adjectives mainly in three places:

- in front of the noun: a <u>desperate</u> attempt

- straight after the noun in a phrase: **The prisoners, <u>desperate</u> to escape, ...**

- after a verb of being, referring to the subject: **The prisoners became <u>desperate</u>.** (See page 23, Complements.)

Pronouns and adjectives

Can an adjective tell us about a pronoun?

Yes, but an adjective is not used before a pronoun in the same way as before a noun. It is normal to write *the happy girl* or *the happy occasion*, but never *happy it* or *happy them*. Occasional exceptions include *lucky you*.

Adjectives are used to describe pronouns in two other ways:

I, <u>happy</u> that my friend seemed unhurt, breathed a sigh of relief.

After the accident, I was <u>happy</u> to see that my friend seemed unhurt.

Other forms of adjectives

Compounds

Words made up of two or three others are called compounds. There are many compound adjectives and, of course, you can make up your own as needed:

brown-haired   soft-centred

high-backed   left-handed

Nouns as adjectives

What part of speech do you think the underlined words are?

a <u>football</u> pitch   the <u>car</u> park

the <u>cinema</u> queue

my <u>music</u> lesson

They are all nouns, but they are being used to tell the reader about other nouns.

It is quite common to find *nouns used as adjectives.* It does not really matter what you call them, so long as you understand the grammar of what is happening.

More participles

Present and past participles were referred to on pages 9–10. These are parts of the verb that cannot stand alone as verbs.

But they do many other things, including working as adjectives. Look at the following:

The <u>defeated</u> and <u>exhausted</u> army returned the <u>following</u> day.

The underlined words are parts of a verb, but are doing the job of adjectives.

Some of these are used so often that they are thought of as adjectives:

embarrassed   charming

amazing   interesting

stressed

Changes in meaning

Sometimes, over time, the meaning of an adjective shifts slightly from the nouns or verbs it is connected with. Sometimes, also, there are two or more adjectives from the same word.

Take the noun *awe*. It means 'wonder or amazement', whether good (admiration) or bad (terror). Two adjectives can be formed from it: *awesome* and *awful*. Think about how they split the meaning into good and bad.

Try it yourself!

What do adjectives look like?

In general, adjectives have nothing in common, but there are some word endings that belong particularly to nouns, others to adjectives and so on. For instance, an adjective might be formed by adding *-ous* to a noun, or a noun formed by adding *-dom* to an adjective. Copy the following chart into your exercise book and fill in the gaps (sometimes there is no suitable verb):

Noun	Adjective	Verb
		free
humour		
tragedy		–
	light	
friend		
		believe
	intelligent	–
		agree
beauty		
help		
		terrify
	decisive	
		dread

Check your answers on **pages 31–32**. All correct?

One or two in the **Verb** column were particularly difficult.

Note that quite often a word takes the same form in different parts of speech.

Adjectives for interest

Though it is misleading to call *all* adjectives 'describing words', that is one of their main jobs. Copy the following piece of writing into your exercise book and liven it up by putting a good descriptive adjective in each of the gaps.

We had never been to Disneyworld before. When we arrived at the _____ park, we were _____ at its _____ variety and size. My younger brother was _____ at the thought of being able to say 'Hi!' to Mickey, but I thought this was rather childish and was more interested in the _____ rides and attractions. As for the Enchanted Castle, that was just _____!

Adverbs

Get started

An **adverb** adds something more about a **verb** just as an **adjective** adds something more about a **noun** or **pronoun**.

Look at the difference between these two sentences:

We caught a <u>slow</u> train from Crewe to Manchester.
The Inter-City express moved <u>slowly</u> through the station.

In the first case, the train always takes a long time and can be described as 'slow'.

In the second case, the fast train was – *at that time and place* – moving slowly. It cannot be described as 'slow'.

Train is a noun and so *slow* is an adjective.

Slowly is not telling the reader about the train, but how it moved. *Moved* is a verb and so *slowly* is an adverb.

Here is an easy way to remember:

Two words beginning with *ad-* 'add' to our knowledge of nouns and verbs. The one that 'adds' information to *verbs* is called an *add-verb*. (But do not forget the correct spelling is *adverb*!)

Practice

Many adverbs are formed from adjectives just by adding *-ly*:

hopeful/hopefully   bright/brightly   intense/intensely   great/greatly

But beware of exceptions:

- Many words exist only as adverbs. Think of *soon* and *often*. In sentences like <u>Soon</u> the bell sounded or I <u>often</u> come here, they add something to the verbs.
- There are some adjectives that do not change at all as adverbs: **These are <u>hard</u> and <u>fast</u> rules** (adjectives) and **He drove <u>hard</u> and <u>fast</u> around the corner** (adverbs).
- *Good* (adjective) and *well* (adverb) are quite different from each other.
- There are many small changes at the end of words before adding *-ly*. For instance, *y* after a consonant becomes *i* (*happy/happily*) and *e* usually disappears (*feeble/feebly*). Most *-ic* words turn into *-ically*: *basic/basically*, *historic/historically*.

Don't forget the adverb

In speech and writing, the most likely mistake is to use an adjective instead of an adverb. This is especially frequent with *good/well*. It is common to hear football managers and television pundits say, 'The boy done good.' There are two mistakes here: it should be *did well* (see page 10), but this is an example that shows clearly the difference between adjectives and adverbs.

Was he a good boy? Possibly, possibly not, but the speaker is not talking about that.

Did he play well? Yes – and that means that the word is describing his action and so is an adverb.

Take care with -ly

Most adverbs end with *-ly*, but, as the text on the left explains, there are plenty of exceptions.

The other problem is that *-ly* is also an adjective ending: *friendly, lively, ugly*.

When you form the adverb from *-ly* adjectives, you have a rather awkward *-lily* ending:

At least we behaved <u>friendlily</u> to each other.

Where do you put the adverb?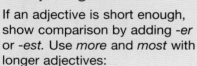

For the most part, put the adverb wherever it sounds best:

<u>Carefully</u>, we worked our way along the ledge.

We worked our way <u>carefully</u> along the ledge.

We worked our way along the ledge <u>carefully</u>.

All are correct. Which sounds best?

However, make certain you place the adverb *only* next to the word it refers to. I <u>only</u> thought two of you were coming means that you only *thought* it (you were not sure). If you are arguing about numbers, it should be I thought <u>only</u> two of you were coming.

Comparing adverbs

If an adjective is short enough, show comparison by adding *-er* or *-est*. Use *more* and *most* with longer adjectives:

neater   quickest

more intelligent

most satisfactory

With some exceptions (*well*, *hard*, *long*, *fast* among them), adverbs always use *more* and *most*:

That was the <u>brightest</u> star in the sky. It shone <u>more brightly</u> than the others.

Try it yourself!

Adjective or adverb?

Turn to the activity on **page 15**.

Make two columns in your exercise book, headed **Adjective** and **Adverb**, then list the adjectives and adverbs in the correct columns. Remember that some words might fit into both columns.

Next, take all the words that appeared only in the **Adjective** column. Turn them all into adverbs and write them in your exercise book.

Check your answers on **pages 31–32**.

All correct?

If not, learn the exceptions. If you could not identify adverbs, move on to the next exercise and practise until you are confident.

Using adverbs

A final check that you are happy using adverbs.

Choose *any three* of the adverbs from the list on **page 15** and use each of them in a sentence in your exercise book.

Activities

Pages 15–18 contain activities based on different sections in the book. You will need to cut up these four pages, so remove them and photocopy them or copy them onto a blank sheet of paper, so that you can do the activities on both sides.

Adjective or adverb? (page 14)

The words listed below are all either adjectives or adverbs or both. Cut them out, then make a pile of all those which can be used as adjectives. When you are happy with your choice, write them in the correct column in your exercise book, as described on page 14. Then do the same for adverbs. Remember, you might be able to put the same word in both piles. If you do not use a word at all, think again! When you have written all the words in the correct column, move on to the next stage.

Take all the words that appear only in the **Adjective** column. Turn them all into adverbs and write them in your exercise book.

Warning: Several of these are exceptions to the normal rule. See if you know them. If not, learn them as exceptions.

tomorrow	full	agreeable	nightly
tightly	comic	again	long
quickly	true	dangerously	only
famous	gloomy	public	calmly
shy	fully	very	solely

Activities

Put them together (page 22)

Below are nouns, pronouns, noun phrases and verbs all jumbled together.
Cut them out and put them in separate piles. The nouns, pronouns and
noun phrases can all be subjects, direct objects or indirect objects. By
moving the words and phrases around, make as many sentences as you
can. Write out in your exercise book:

- sentences where you can reverse subject and object, for example:
  The lion frightened the hunter.   The hunter frightened the lion.
- sentences with both direct and indirect objects.

the lion	what to do	I	the bus
gave	him	caught	a chance
offered	frightened	knew	the hunter
a medal	the late goal	won	praised
celebrated	the mayor	wondered	a fight
the architect	my brother	awarded	followed
the quarrel	whether to go	worried	the new tram
outperformed	you	paid	his fee

Activities

Mixing the sentences (page 26)

Below you will find a mixture of parts of sentences. Some are verbs, so you will know what their part in a sentence will be. Some are nouns or noun phrases, so they could be subjects or objects or complements. Adjectives will need a noun to relate to and adverbs will probably be used with a verb, adjective or adverb.

You will probably find it easiest to start with all the words and phrases in piles according to parts of speech. Then create, and write out in your exercise book, four sentences:

1 with a verb of being and complement
2 with a verb of doing, direct and indirect objects
3 as 1, but with at least one adverb or adverb phrase
4 as 2, but with at least one adverb or adverb phrase.

Then assemble as many words and phrases as you can to create the longest sentence that makes sense.

every May	in the park	carefully	brought
was smiling	Mr Shah	happy	his lorry
across the river	in a temper	they	were
became	gently	seems	too late
Tony	quietly	offered	the school
in the garden	gave	the children	after work
advice	in the rain	at five o'clock	I
shouted	a party	a warning	generously

Activities

Cut and change (page 30)

Below are six sentences. All of them are complex sentences with two clauses joined by a conjunction (which may not be in the middle, remember). Then there is a list of subordinating conjunctions. Cut out the conjunctions, then try them in each of the sentences to see if they make sense. Write out at least one alternative version of each sentence (two or three if possible) in your exercise book, explaining what sort of connection you have made. Cut up the sentences to alter the order of the clauses if you wish. An example is given on page 30.

If the teacher asked me, I helped to collect in the books.

We had no hope of winning after Jane was dropped from the team.

After he made the announcement, we all knew the bad news.

Before he made the announcement, no one knew the bad news.

We were in trouble until Ben joined the expedition.

I applied to Mayfield School because Mrs Schofield was the head.

if	after	where	before	because	until	though
as	when	unless	since	although	while	

Forming sentences: subject and verb

Get started

The second half of this book deals with forming sentences. How do the main parts of speech fit together to make a sentence?

The shortest sentence consists simply of a **subject** (a **noun** or **pronoun**) and a **verb**.

The finger beckoned.	**Night fell.**
Tom was running.	**My mother laughed.**
I lost.	

These are all very short, but they *are* sentences because they make sense on their own.

Practice

- A verb can be one word or two or more (such as *was running*). (Remember **continuous tenses** and **auxiliary verbs** from **pages 9–10**?)
- A verb relates to a particular time, and so is in a certain **tense**.
- A verb must be capable of following a subject. This means that some parts of the verb (like **participles**) are not suitable. *Running* can refer to different times (*is running*, *was running*, *will be running*) and does not make sense after a subject (*I running*, *Mr McAvoy running*) – unless with another verb (*Mr McAvoy was running*).

- A subject can be a single-word noun or pronoun or a single noun with a definite or indefinite article (*the car*, *an accident*, *a fire*).
- A subject can also be a noun with an adjective or adjectives added before or, less often, after (*The long, black car . . .* or *A fire, warm and cosy, . . .*).
- A subject can be a phrase which has no single main noun in it, but which does the job of a noun. Look at this example: **How to stop losing money was the main point of discussion.** If you put the adjectives and noun *Our financial loss* as the subject, it would make similar sense. So *How to stop losing money* is a **noun phrase**, doing the job of a noun as subject of the sentence.

The principle is easy: there might be all sorts of extra bits added on, but the simplest sentence is basically just **subject/verb**.

A question of sentences

This section concentrates on sentences that are **statements**.

Do not forget that sentences can be **questions** and **commands** too.

In many ways, questions and commands are the same as statements, but, apart from things like question marks, there is one important difference in each case:

- Questions – Often a verb is divided up in a question. A statement may say, I had a good time on holiday. For a question, *had* is divided into *did have*: Did you have a good time on holiday?
- Commands – These are the only full sentences without subjects. If you are giving an order, there is no need to say who is doing the action. It is obvious – it is the person you are talking to. A statement says, Carl had to tidy his bedroom before going out. The command Carl received was Tidy your bedroom before you go out.

Verbs: complete and incomplete

Some verbs are complete in themselves:

All my friends <u>came</u>.

In winter the ice <u>froze</u>.

The wind <u>howled</u> and the thunder <u>rumbled</u>.

But many verbs need something added to make sense:

My mother <u>caught</u> . . .

Caught what? The bus, a cold or you misbehaving?

Our class was told to <u>bring</u> . . .

Bring what? Homework, nature specimens or money for the class trip?

Think what verbs like *catch* and *bring* need to complete a sentence.

Now see page 21.

Try it yourself!

Find the sentences

Remember:
- All sentences except commands have a subject (a noun or word/s doing the job of a noun) and a verb which relates to a time (e.g. past tense).
- Commands do not need a subject.

In the examples that follow, some are sentences, some are not. Copy them all into your exercise book. Then, after each one, indicate **statement** (S), **question** (Q), **command** (C) or **not a sentence** (NS). If you think it is a sentence, mark the **subject** and the **verb** by underlining or ringing.

Some of the subjects and verbs consist of more than one word, so mark both or all the words. There are other parts to the sentences – just ignore these.

> Sangeeta and Kate went to the same school.
> Outside the cinema.
> Buying an ice cream from the supermarket.
> I will see you tomorrow.
> Did the boy bring the right paper?
> How could the referee see from there?
> A pint of milk, please.
> Pass me the milk, please.
> Digging the garden tired me out.
> Say good morning to Mr Howells.
> I want you to meet Mr Howells.
> Mr Howells to see you.
> Why did you wake me so early?
> Half past seven.
> To get all the answers right is difficult.

Check your answers on **pages 31–32**.

All correct?

If so, congratulations. One or two of those were very difficult.

Do not worry if you missed those long phrases as subjects. However, if you made any mistakes about which were sentences, compare your answers to the definition of what makes a sentence (**page 19** and the top of this page).

Direct and indirect objects

Get started

Some actions are complete in themselves; some are complete only if there is a person or thing for the action to be done to.

This 'done to' part of the sentence is called the **direct object**:

> I handed <u>my book</u> in.
> The production toured <u>the country</u>.
> My mother bought <u>a bright red car</u>.
> I knew <u>what to expect</u>.

It is fairly straightforward, except for that awkward phrase in the last sentence. Remember that the sentence could be **I knew** <u>the answer</u>, with *answer* doing just the same job as *what to expect*.

Practice

What is the object in this sentence?

> **I gave the teacher my book.**

Who or what is on the end of the giving: the teacher or the book?

In fact, both are the objects of the sentence:

- The **direct object** has the action done directly to it/him/her/them. In this case, *my book* was lifted up and passed from hand to hand.
- If someone/something receives the direct object, he/she/it is called the **indirect object**.

A good way to identify an indirect object is to remember that, if the direct object goes first, the indirect object follows the word *to*.

Does it make sense to write: **I gave my book to the teacher**? Yes.

Does it make sense to write: **I gave the teacher to my book**? Not really.

Therefore *book* is the direct object and *teacher* the indirect object.

Remember, though, that *to* is not necessary if the indirect object goes first.

Verbs: complete and incomplete (continued)

Some verbs need a direct object to complete the action. *He ran* makes sense, but *he threw* inspires the question *what*?

However, verbs do not divide simply into those that have an object and those that do not. Many verbs can do either:

When he was feeling energetic, he ran to school.

Our neighbours ran a shop.

In the second example, *ran* has an object: *shop*.

And there are plenty more:

He tried hard.

He tried a piece of my cake.

I sat in the train.

My father sat me down and explained the problem., etc., etc., etc.

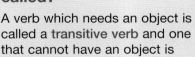

What are these verbs called?

A verb which needs an object is called a **transitive verb** and one that cannot have an object is **intransitive**.

As mentioned above, many verbs can be either transitive or intransitive.

A first word about prepositions

Prepositions are often very short, but they are very important in making sentences work. A preposition is placed before a noun or pronoun to join it to the rest of the sentence. So far, we have met *to* which can be used to link an indirect object to the rest of a sentence.

You can probably think of other uses *to* has.

Can you think of some other prepositions?

Words and phrases

Noun phrases were mentioned on page 19.

A phrase is a group of words, but not a full sentence.

These groups of words do the job of a particular part of speech, so there are also adjective phrases and adverb phrases.

For example, you could describe a man by writing *the strong man*, using an adjective. If you wrote *the man with muscles like iron*, that would be an adjective phrase.

Try it yourself!

Put them together

Turn to the activity on **page 16**.

You will see a page full of nouns, pronouns, noun phrases and verbs.

Your task is to put them together in as many sentences as you can, all consisting of subject – verb – direct object, or subject – verb – indirect object – direct object.

Write the sentences in your exercise book and try to find as many cases as you can:
- where you can reverse the sentence, turning subject into object and object into subject
- where there are all four parts: subject, verb, direct object and indirect object.

Compare your answers to the suggestions on **pages 31–32**.

Watch out for pronouns

Pronouns take a different form depending on whether they are subject or object:

<u>She</u> took <u>me</u> to the park.   <u>I</u> took <u>her</u> to the park.

Copy the following sentences into your exercise book, writing out the correct pronoun as you go:

The taxi collected (they/them) at the airport.
Joanna's aunt sent (she/her) a birthday card.
Jack and (I/me) were playing by the river.
The invitation was addressed to my brother and (I/me).
(She/her) expected (I/me) to help (she/her) with her homework.

Check your answers on **pages 31–32**.

All correct?

Most were very easy, but some people have a problem when *I* or *me* follows a noun and *and*. The rule is quite simple: use the same pronoun as if the noun was not there. **The invitation was addressed to I** is obviously wrong, so do not write **The invitation was addressed to my brother and I.**

Complements

Get started

Though it is possible to imagine a situation where *I am!* becomes a full statement, generally verbs of being need something else to complete their meaning:

Maya became   **Natasha seems**   **Mr Brown was**

These subject/verb combinations do not mean anything.

But what can be added to a verb of being? Not an object because that is 'done to' by the verb and a verb of being cannot *do* anything.

What is needed is a **complement**.

Practice

A complement is something that *completes*.

	Subject	Verb	Complement
Noun complements	That man	was	my father.
	The school	became	a youth centre.

- The complement is equivalent to the subject, the same person or thing.

Adjective complements	That man	is	very tall.
	The school	seemed	empty.

- The complement says something about the subject.

Adverb complements	That man	was	on the plane.
	The school	is	behind the bus station.

Do not worry if you cannot tell the difference between noun, adjective and adverb complements: the exercises on **page 24** will help you with that. Just make sure that you are confident with these common forms of sentences:

subject – verb of doing – (indirect object) – direct object

subject – verb of being – complement

More prepositions

There are two prepositions in the table about complements: *on* and *behind*.

Prepositions are often used in adverb phrases to make the link with the rest of the sentence, and that link is important in showing the meaning. Just look at this obvious example:

in

under

My pen was behind the desk.

on

near

The prepositions do not just join *the desk* to the rest of the sentence. They also tell the reader how it fits in with everything else.

To be really correct...

Complements refer back to the subject; noun complements are essentially the same as the subject. So, if a pronoun is used for the noun complement, it really should be in the subject form:

It is I is strictly correct, not **It's me.**

In formal writing, stick to the rules. However, there are cases where it would just sound odd.

Not so simple

The structure of a sentence can sound very simple. When faced with a sentence on a page, however, it can be much more difficult to see the structure clearly. This is often because long phrases can do the job of subject, object or complement. Nouns might be surrounded by adjectives or adjective phrases.

Take the simple sentence:

The problem was difficult.

Enlarge or replace subject and complement with complicated phrases:

The most urgent problem before the committee was a consideration of the losses sustained at last year's event.

It is still the same structure: subject – verb – complement.

Wait and see

Adverbs are not always used as complements. The other parts they can play in a sentence can make simple sentences more complicated. Do not worry: the next section (page 25) deals with adverbs.

Try it yourself!

Choose your complement

In the following sentences, there is a subject followed by a verb of being. Copy each sentence into your exercise book and complete it by adding a complement of the type stated, choosing from the list below:

Mrs Ackroyd became _____. (noun complement)

Mrs Ackroyd became _____. (adjective complement)

His walking stick was _____. (noun complement)

His walking stick was _____. (adjective complement)

His walking stick was _____. (adverb complement)

Hannah seemed _____. (adjective complement)

The holiday in Greece was _____. (adverb complement)

The holiday in Greece was _____. (adjective complement)

The holiday in Greece was _____. (noun complement)

Yesterday's news has become _____. (adjective complement)

Brazil became _____. (noun complement)

Brazil appeared _____. (adjective complement)

Brazil was _____. (adverb complement)

London is _____. (noun complement)

London is _____. (adverb complement)

London is _____. (adjective complement)

> head of the company   in England's group   in the brochure
> expensive   extremely agitated   made of oak   happy
> my first choice   the capital city   world champions   in the hall
> unbeatable   his proudest possession   boring   in the South
> very busy

Check your answers on **pages 31–32**.

All correct?

Just check that you understand this by creating another ending for each of the sentences above and writing these in your exercise book. You could begin:

Mrs Ackroyd became <u>the county librarian</u>. (noun complement)
Mrs Ackroyd became <u>worried about funding</u>. (adjective complement)
. . . and so on. See how well you can do.

How to use adverbs

Get started

You can use an **adverb** or **adverb phrase** in any sentence. All sentences contain **verbs**, so there is every chance the writer might want to say more about the verb. Anything that gives more information about the verb is an adverb or (very often) an adverb phrase.

Practice

Look at this sentence. It takes the simplest subject – verb – direct object form:

The cinema shows films.

It makes sense, but it does not really say anything.

Add some bits to the nouns: an adjective (*new*), an adjective phrase (*in the shopping centre*) and a noun used as an adjective (*horror*):

The new cinema in the shopping centre shows horror films.

This is better, but there is a need for still more information. That is where adverbs come in. Mostly, adverbs and adverb phrases answer questions like: *When? Where? How? Why?*

As a matter of policy, the new cinema in the shopping centre regularly shows horror films on Friday afternoons in Screen Two.

Do the same thing for a typical subject – verb – complement sentence:

Rafik became terrified.

It makes sense, but it is short and unhelpful. Add the adverbs and adverb phrases:

At the fair, Rafik quickly became terrified of the ghost train.

Imagine the subject – verb – complement or subject – verb – object structure as being like a skeleton, a framework. If you want to build on it, there is plenty you can add, but you need to be aware of the skeleton underneath. Sometimes adding adverbs and adverb phrases is essential: in the example above, you would not know when to go to see the horror films without them. At other times, these extra details can add interest – so long as they are not overdone.

Adverb phrases

Remember that an adverb phrase does not have to include an adverb, just as noun phrases and adjective phrases do not always include nouns or adjectives. It simply has to do the *job* of an adverb.

I'll do the shopping <u>soon</u>.

Soon is an adverb. Now look at the following sentence:

I'll do the shopping <u>in ten minutes</u>.

In ten minutes consists of a preposition, an adjective and a noun, but it is serving as an adverb, so it is an adverb phrase.

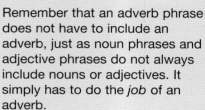

Other jobs for adverbs

Adverbs are also used:

- with adjectives – To say more about an adjective, use an adverb: *very unpleasant*, *hopelessly inefficient*, *seriously ill*.
- with adverbs – The same as with adjectives: *painfully slowly*, *fairly capably*.

Here are some examples:

The <u>quietly</u> confident contestant smiled <u>calmly</u>.

This sentence contains two adverbs: one describes how he *smiled* (verb), the other how *confident* (adjective) he was. It would also have made sense to use the phrase *calmly confident contestant*. In this example, *calmly* relates to the adjective.

It hurt <u>dreadfully</u>.

It happened <u>dreadfully</u> quickly.

Here the same adverb is used in both sentences: in one case it tells about a verb (*hurt*), in the other it tells about an adverb (*quickly*).

Adverbs and whole sentences

You may be confused sometimes by finding what is obviously an adverb, but with no verb, adjective or adverb to relate to. *Oddly*, adverbs sometimes relate to the whole sentence. (And the sentence you have just read is an example of this!)

Again, examples are the easiest way to make this clear. Look at the word *clearly* (an adverb) in these two sentences:

Julia wrote very <u>clearly</u>.

This is normal adverbial use: the adverb describes the verb *wrote* – everyone could read her writing.

<u>Clearly</u> Julia had written to the police.

This says nothing about what her writing was like or whether it was easy to read. Instead, *clearly* suggests there is evidence that Julia had made contact with the police. In other words, it says that the whole sentence must have happened.

It is the same idea here:

<u>Surprisingly</u> I did well in the test.
<u>Obviously</u> I must be intelligent.

Try it yourself!

Mixing the sentences

Covering the main parts of what is called a **simple sentence** has proved that it is not always so simple. The pattern is something like this:

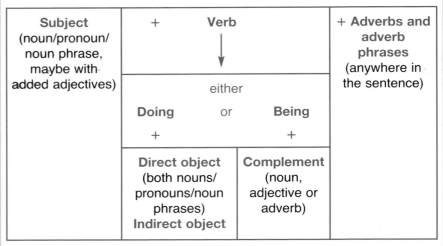

Subject (noun/pronoun/ noun phrase, maybe with added adjectives)	+ Verb either Doing or Being +		+ Adverbs and adverb phrases (anywhere in the sentence)
	Direct object (both nouns/ pronouns/noun phrases) Indirect object	Complement (noun, adjective or adverb)	

The activity you are going to do consists of taking all these elements and creating as many (long!) sentences as you can.

Turn to the activity on **page 17**.

Follow the instructions there, then write out a sentence in your exercise book:
- **with a verb of being and complement**
- **with a verb of doing and direct or indirect objects**
- **as the first sentence above, but with at least one adverb or adverb phrase**
- **as the second sentence above, but with at least one adverb or adverb phrase**
- **as long as you can build that still makes sense.**

Compare your answers to the suggestions on **pages 31–32**.

Are you happy with your answers?

Making the longest sentence you can is a useful way of showing how sentences work – and it can be fun.

But it is not the way to write well! In your own writing, make sure you have a good balance of short and long sentences, and avoid rambling and *confused* sentences.

Joining sentences: compounds

Get started

All the sentences dealt with so far have been **simple sentences**. Some of them may have seemed complicated, but they all have one thing in common:

They include only one verb with a subject and refer to a set time.

Sometimes you want to use more than one such verb.

In that case, you need to use a word that joins together two sentences. You may have come across various names for these words: *joining word*, *connective*, *connecting word*, and – the one used here – **conjunction**. If you think of the meanings of *join*, *junction* and *connect*, you will easily see what these words do.

Practice

Before going on, read the note **What is a clause?** on the right.

The simplest way of joining clauses is to join two **equal clauses** with a conjunction which gives no suggestion of which half is more important. The main conjunctions of this sort are:

- *but*:   the two clauses contradict each other
- *so*:   the first clause is a reason for the second
- *or*:   the two clauses are alternatives
- *and*:   the most common conjunction, which says absolutely nothing about the clauses except that they are joined together.

Making compound sentences is quite easy. Using them effectively is a little more difficult.

- A very common error is to simply write clause after clause with commas between them and no conjunctions. This is simply wrong (but see **An exception** on **page 28**).
- Something that is not wrong, but makes writing boring and tedious to read, is using *and* constantly. Try for some variety; the next section will deal with many more conjunctions.

What is a clause?

Put simply, a **clause** is something that is, or could have been, a sentence. A clause is a group of words with the crucial subject – verb combination.

So *going to the supermarket* is not a clause, but *I am going to the supermarket* is.

A **simple sentence** consists of one main clause.

A **compound sentence** (dealt with here) consists of two or more main clauses (sometimes called **coordinate clauses**).

A **complex sentence** (dealt with on page 29) consists of a main clause and one or more less important clauses – known as subordinate clauses.

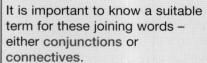

Are the names important?

It is important to know a suitable term for these joining words – either **conjunctions** or **connectives**.

It is less important (but can be interesting) to know that the sorts of conjunctions described in this section are called **coordinating conjunctions** and the ones in the next section are **subordinating conjunctions**.

A little extra meaning

Sometimes the conjunction you use can tell the reader a little bit extra. This is much more the case with complex sentences (see page 29), but it does happen with compound sentences.

Look at the following example:

The party was at Becky's <u>so</u> I decided to go.

The party was at Becky's, <u>but</u> I decided to go.

What does the choice of conjunction say about the speaker's feelings towards Becky?

An exception

Usually it is not correct to separate clauses by commas with no conjunctions. With more than two clauses, however, it is correct to save *and* until before the last one, just like in a list: . . . salt, pepper, brown sauce <u>and</u> vinegar.

So it is wrong to say: Ashok went into the shop, he bought a chocolate bar.

But this is fine: Ashok went into the shop, bought a chocolate bar <u>and</u> paid for it out of his pocket money.

Try it yourself!

Forming compound sentences

Put a conjunction in the middle of the following pairs of simple sentences (and one group of three) and write out the full sentences in your exercise book. Decide which is the best conjunction; do not just put *and* every time.

> The bell sounded . . . the teacher continued with the lesson.
>
> The bell sounded . . . the teacher told the class to stop work.
>
> The bell sounded . . . the lights flashed.
>
> The bell sounded . . . the lights flashed . . . the gates closed.
>
> Did I hear the bell . . . was that somebody's mobile phone?
>
> It was Sunday . . . I decided to stay in bed.
>
> I thought I knew the way . . . I took the wrong path through the woods.
>
> I'll take a map next time . . . I might get lost again.

Check your answers on **pages 31–32. All correct?**

If not, make sure that you know what your mistake was, then move on to something a bit more difficult.

Is there something shorter?

The simplest way to join two or more sentences is to connect them up with a conjunction and make no other change except removing a capital letter.

There are other ways, for instance, cutting down the number of clauses by getting rid of one of the subject – verb units.

For example: **I hurried to catch the bus. I bumped into an old lady.**

Turn the first verb into a participle (see **page 10**): **Hurrying to catch the bus, I bumped into an old lady.**

. . . or get rid of it altogether: **In my hurry to catch the bus, I bumped into an old lady.**

What would you do with these?
> The new hospital has more beds. It will serve the community more successfully.
> You can buy groceries at the new supermarket. They are much cheaper.
> My mother checked her mirrors. She pulled out into the traffic.

Compare your answers with those on **pages 31–32.**

Complex sentences

Get started

To create a **complex sentence** you need to:
- decide what is the most important clause
- decide how any other clauses fit in with it
- choose your **conjunction** to show that connection.

Suppose you had a music lesson on Saturday morning, then in the afternoon you went shopping. Which is the more important? That depends on the story you are telling:

> <u>Before</u> I went shopping, I had my music lesson. Mrs Blake gave me a new piece to practise.
> <u>After</u> I had my music lesson, I went shopping. I bought a new CD and some books.

What is the reason for the choice of main clause each time? The first story goes on to tell about the music lesson, so that is the main interest. The second one tells of your shopping trip, so the sentence is the other way round.

The connection made here (obviously enough) is of *time*.

Practice

Some of the connections conjunctions can make between main and subordinate clauses are of:

Time	when, before, after, whenever, while, as, since, until
Place	where
Reason	because, as, since (*note* – some conjunctions have two meanings)
Possibility	if, unless
Contrast	though, although

The first job of a conjunction or connective is (just like the names say) to join or to connect.

But connections can be made for different reasons, at different angles, in different places.

Start with the statement **I was really happy last Saturday.**

What sort of connection makes sense?
- Time? **<u>When</u> I got my new bike, . . .**
- Reason? **. . . <u>because</u> my tickets for the concert arrived.**
- Or perhaps mentioning something less happy? **. . . <u>although</u> I'm not looking forward to going back to school.**

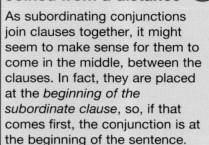

Joined from a distance

As subordinating conjunctions join clauses together, it might seem to make sense for them to come in the middle, between the clauses. In fact, they are placed at the *beginning of the subordinate clause*, so, if that comes first, the conjunction is at the beginning of the sentence.

> I took the book off the shelf <u>and</u> I found the cover was torn.

But

> <u>When</u> I took the book off the shelf, I found the cover was torn.

Another difficult term

It is important to use conjunctions accurately, but it is also interesting to know the correct term for the conjunctions in this section.

A *subordinate* is someone or something in a lower position, so the less important clauses are **subordinate clauses** and words like *although*, *when* and *because* are **subordinating conjunctions**.

How does this affect my writing?

The way you write in stories and other compositions can be improved by knowledge of different forms of sentences.

This is not to say that you should use really long sentences all the time. Sometimes (like when you wish to suggest pace and excitement) short sentences are best.

Most pieces of writing are more interesting if you use a *variety* of sentence types.

What's this?

The last two sections dealt with compound sentences (two equal clauses) and complex sentences (one main clause and one or more subordinate clauses). But what about sentences like this one?

We ran to the bus station and caught the coach to Bridlington as it was pulling out.

Surely this is both – it has *and* and it has *as*.

Quite correct – believe it or not, this is a **compound-complex sentence!**

Try it yourself!

Alter the meaning

The conjunction you use can have a big effect on the meaning of the sentence. It can even tell you something about the characters involved.

Look at these two statements:

I went to the cinema.   There was a horror film showing.

By your use of conjunctions, you can alter the whole sense. Choose a conjunction to fit with the instruction at the end of each line and write your completed sentences in your exercise book:

I went to the cinema . . . there was a horror film showing. (You like horror films.)

I went to the cinema . . . there was a horror film showing. (You dislike horror films.)

I went to the cinema . . . there was a horror film showing. (You refuse to watch horror.)

I went to the cinema . . . there was a horror film showing. (Horror is all you watch.)

Check your answers on pages 31–32. Make sure you have grasped the idea before you try the last activity.

Cut and change

Turn to the activity on page 18.

You have a number of complex sentences to cut up. Cut each one into separate clauses and conjunctions, then change the conjunctions and change the meaning. (Full instructions are on page 18.)

Here is an example of the sort of answer you should give:

Because the teacher asked me, I helped to collect in the books. (gives a reason)

Write out your alternative versions in your exercise book.

Compare your answers with those on pages 31–32.

Your answers do not need to be identical, but you should now know something of the ways conjunctions join together compound and complex sentences.

Answers

FIND THE NOUNS (PAGE 4)

Common nouns: match, park, character, book, lesson, day, parents, brother

Proper nouns: Brentford, Barnet, Ahmed, Harry Potter, English, Spain, Greece

FILL IN THE CHART (PAGE 6)

There is obviously room for many variations, especially with proper nouns, but here is some guidance:

Common	Proper	Collective
soldier	Sergeant Marshall	platoon/battalion/army
pupil	Fiona	class
musician/guitarist	Jools Holland	band
book	The Two Towers	library
politician	Tony Blair	party/parliament/cabinet
footballer/player	David Beckham	team
deer/fawn	Bambi	herd
singer	Charlotte Church	choir/chorus
teacher	Mrs Silverwood	staff
ship	Ark Royal	fleet/navy

A QUICK LOOK AT PRONOUNS (PAGE 6)

I, this, what, it, who, them, it (in *It's*), they, me, I, any, you (in *you've*), them, all, he, something, I, it

Most of these are obvious, but some are very difficult. *What* is used in a question and you can see that it is taking the place of a noun by looking at the answer: '*What is it?*' '*It's* <u>an old copy</u> . . .' *Who* is a joining word that takes the place of *he* in that sentence. Also, you need to imagine *any*, *all* and *something* being replaced by nouns; they are all objects.

FIRST FIND THE VERB . . . (PAGE 8)

caught, drives, seemed, opened, became, slipped

A QUICK CHECK (PAGE 8)

being, doing, doing, being, doing, being, doing, being

COMPLETE THE CHART (PAGE 10)

	Present	Simple past	Perfect
try	tries	tried	has tried
lie	lies	lay	has lain
lie	lies	lied	has lied
lay	lays	laid	has laid
force	forces	forced	has forced
join	joins	joined	has joined
beat	beats	beat	has beaten
enjoy	enjoys	enjoyed	has enjoyed
be	is	was	has been
grow	grows	grew	has grown
keep	keeps	kept	has kept
note	notes	noted	has noted
write	writes	wrote	has written
bite	bites	bit	has bitten
do	does	did	has done
show	shows	showed	has shown
insist	insists	insisted	has insisted
run	runs	ran	has run
draw	draws	drew	has drawn

WHAT DO ADJECTIVES LOOK LIKE? (PAGE 12)

Noun	Adjective	Verb
freedom	free	free
humour	humorous	humour
tragedy	tragic	–
lightness (or light)	light	lighten (or enlighten)
friend	friendly	befriend
belief	believable	believe
intelligence	intelligent	–
agreement	agreeable	agree
beauty	beautiful	beautify
help	helpful (or helpless)	help
terror	terrific	terrify
decision	decisive	decide
dread	dreadful	dread

ADJECTIVE OR ADVERB? (PAGE 14)

Adjectives: full, agreeable, nightly, comic, long, true, only, famous, gloomy, public, shy

Adverbs: tomorrow, full, nightly, tightly, again, long, quickly, dangerously, only, calmly, fully, very, solely (Note: *Full* and *fully* are both adverbs, *full* can also be an adjective.)

Adjectives into adverbs: agreeably, comically, truly, famously, gloomily, publicly, shyly

(Note: *Publicly* and *shyly* are both exceptions to the rule.)

Answers

FIND THE SENTENCES (PAGE 20)

S (Sangeeta and Kate/went), NS, NS, S (I/will see), Q (the boy/did bring), Q (the referee/could see), NS, C (no subject/pass), S (digging the garden/tired), C (no subject/say), S (I/want), NS, Q (you/did wake), NS, S (to get all the answers right/is)

PUT THEM TOGETHER (PAGE 22)

You may find more than this, but here are some examples of sentences which can be reversed:
The new tram outperformed the bus. The bus outperformed the new tram.
The mayor praised the architect. The architect praised the mayor.
My brother knew the mayor. The mayor knew my brother.
You followed my brother. My brother followed you.
Sentences with both direct and indirect objects include:
The hunter gave the lion a chance (and other similar ones including: I gave him a chance)
The mayor gave him a medal.
The mayor paid the architect his fee.
The late goal gave my brother a medal.
The mayor awarded my brother a medal.

WATCH OUT FOR PRONOUNS (PAGE 22)

them; her; I; me; she, me, her

CHOOSE YOUR COMPLEMENT (PAGE 24)

Here are some suggestions:

head of the company, extremely agitated, his proudest possession, made of oak, in the hall, happy, in the brochure, expensive, my first choice, boring, world champions, unbeatable, in England's group, the capital city, in the South, very busy

MIXING THE SENTENCES (PAGE 26)

Here are some suggestions:

Tony became happy.
The school offered the children a party.
Mr Shah seems in a temper in the garden.
Too late, Tony gave the children advice.
Every May, at five o'clock after work, Mr Shah generously gave the children a party in the park across the river.

FORMING COMPOUND SENTENCES (PAGE 28)

but, so, and, comma/and, or, so, but, or

IS THERE SOMETHING SHORTER? (PAGE 28)

Here are some suggestions:

With more beds the new hospital will serve the community more successfully.
You can buy much cheaper groceries at the new supermarket.
Having checked her mirrors, my mother pulled out into the traffic.

ALTER THE MEANING (PAGE 30)

because/as, although, unless, if/whenever

CUT AND CHANGE (PAGE 30)

Here are some suggestions:
When (or *After*) the teacher asked me, I helped to collect in the books. (time)
Before the teacher asked me, I helped to collect in the books. (time, showing your character)
Although the teacher asked me, I helped to collect in the books. (contrast, suggests you don't like the teacher)
We had no hope of winning *unless/before/until* Jane was dropped from the team. (three ways of suggesting Jane is the weak link)
We had no hope of winning *when* Jane was dropped from the team. (time)
We had no hope of winning *while* Jane was dropped from the team. (time, suggesting Jane, the star player, will come back)
Although Jane was dropped from the team, we had no hope of winning. (complicated, suggesting Jane is the weak link, but the team's pretty bad too)
We all knew the bad news *before* he made the announcement. (time)
Since he made the announcement, we all knew the bad news. (reason)
Until he made the announcement, no one knew the bad news. (time)
No one knew the bad news *although* he made the announcement. (contrast)
We were in trouble *before/when* Ben joined the expedition. (time)
Because Ben joined the expedition, we were in trouble. (reason)
We were in trouble *if/unless* Ben joined the expedition. (two different possibilities – is Ben any good?)
I applied to Mayfield School *where* Mrs Schofield was the head. (place)
I applied to Mayfield School *when/after/before* Mrs Schofield was the head. (various different times)
Although Mrs Schofield was the head, I applied to Mayfield School. (contrast, suggesting you don't like Mrs Schofield)

Note how your choice of subordinating conjunctions can reveal what you think about Jane, Ben and Mrs Schofield.